Meet ELFIE!

She is hiding on each page, so be sure to look out for her!

Can You Spot?

Magical World

An enchanting search-and-find book

Written by Laura Jackson & illustrated by Sophie Hanton

Contents

Get ready for an adventure!

Elfie the fairy is about to go on a magical journey
to visit friends far and wide. And she
wants you to come along, too.

Get ready to explore a world of mermaids, unicorns,
princesses and giants as you search for animals, objects,
magical creatures and fantastical friends.

Watch out for Elfie hiding on each page, too. She could be
anywhere in the ice kingdoms, cloud palaces, spell rooms
and fairy-tale worlds.

Friends to find

Here are some friends you will meet along the way!

Blossom

This sweet unicorn loves to take Elfie on rides through the clouds.

WHIZZ!

SNAP!

Wizard Whizzbang

Full of magic and mischief, Wizard Whizzbang loves to turn his treetop world upside down with spells!

The Big, Bad Wolf

Uh, oh. Elfie needs to stay well away from this ferocious wolf. He likes to go SNAP!

BANG!

Wanda Witch

Nervous and sweet, this little witch often gets her spells wrong. Her potions always end with a BANG!

Luna

Luna the mermaid loves to dive and dip under the glow of the moonlight.

Sunshine Fairy

Spreading happiness and sunshine wherever she goes, Elfie loves to play with the Sunshine Fairy every day.

BRRR!

The Ice Queen

Ruler of the frozen world, Elfie is a bit scared of the queen's strong powers. The queen has an icy touch!

What are you waiting for? There's a world of magic to explore. Let's go!

Unicorn Land

Little fairy Elfie watches unicorns gather round
A bubbling, magic waterfall that splashes on the ground.

Can you spot?

Queen of the Unicorns

Blossom

Rainbow Shine

Sparkle

3 bunnies   5 white doves   6 owls   7 blue baby unicorns   8 water fairies

Treetop Travels

Elfie flies up higher to a busy treetop town,
She lands up at the top, then slip-slides right back down!

Can you spot?

Teapot house   Wizard Whizzbang   Madame Make-a-lot   2 gnomes

3 pots of nettle soup

4 red squirrels

5 swinging pixies

6 dusting fairies

7 wizard flags

Once Upon a Time

In a land far, far away, Elfie finds a comfy spot,
But watch out for The Wicked Witch, bubbling potions in a pot!

Can you spot?

Little Red Riding Hood

Goldilocks

The Big, Bad Wolf

Humpty Dumpty

The Wicked Witch

2 handsome princes

3 little pigs

5 gingerbread men

9 princess crowns

Cloud Magic

Up, up and away! Elfie flies up in the sky,
To a palace in the clouds, floating way up high.

Can you spot?

Cloud Wizard　　　Sunshine Fairy　　　an angry elf　　　Rainbow Bird

2 lollipop trees   3 baby dragons   4 sleeping pixies   5 cloud fairies   8 cloud candy sticks

Under the Sea

Elfie dives down deep to the ocean blue,
To say 'hello' to mermaids and all the narwhals too.

Can you spot?

King Neptune

Princess Atlanta

Splash

Luna

Gem   2 treasure chests   3 pink seahorses   4 snappy lobsters   5 baby narwhals

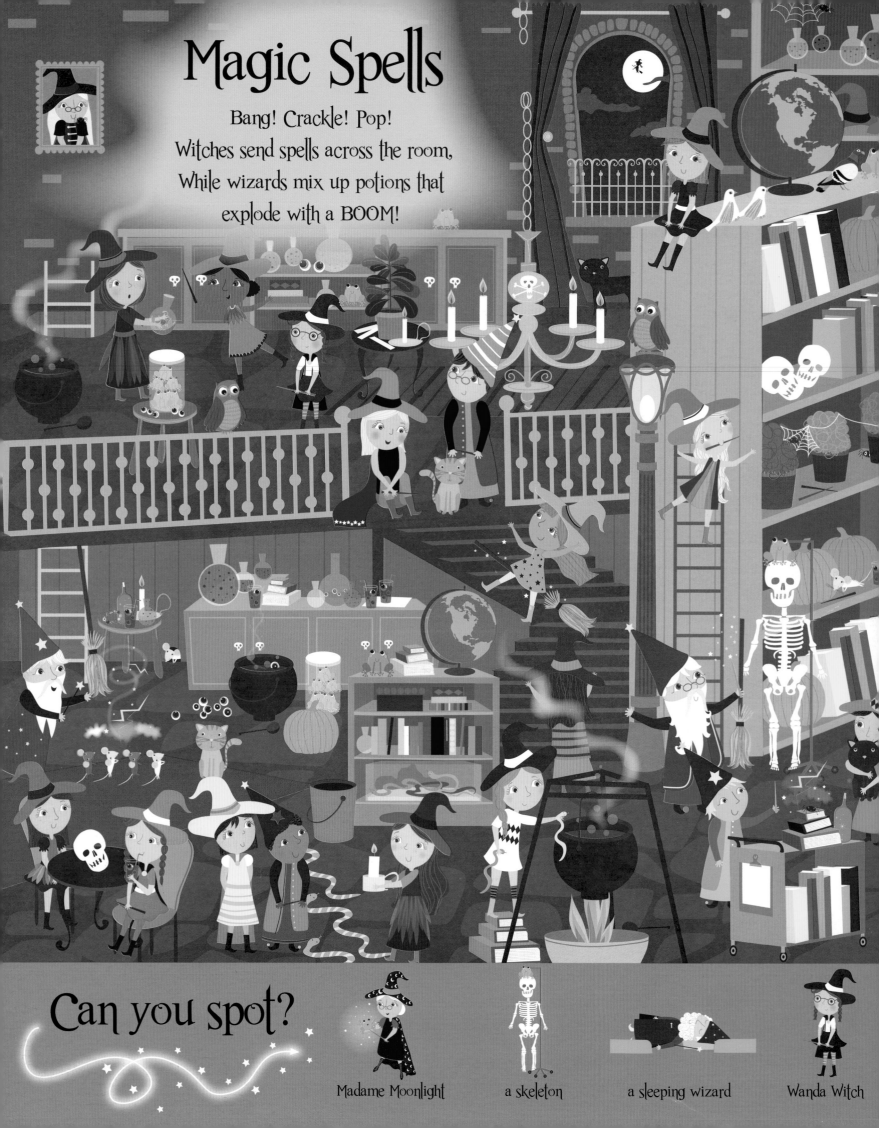

Magic Spells

Bang! Crackle! Pop!
Witches send spells across the room,
While wizards mix up potions that
explode with a BOOM!

Can you spot?

Madame Moonlight

a skeleton

a sleeping wizard

Wanda Witch

 5 black cats

 6 jars of frogs

 7 bubbling cauldrons

 8 broomsticks

 10 pumpkins

Ice World

It's always winter in this land, filled with frost and snow.
It's way too cold for Elfie, it's time for her to go!

Can you spot?

The Ice Queen

Princess Star

Frosty

Snow Bear

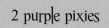 2 purple pixies

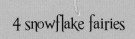 4 snowflake fairies

5 twinkling diamonds

 7 baby penguins

 8 frosty cupcakes

Home, Sweet Home

Little fairy Elfie lands in her
home within the trees,
Just in time to party with the
unicorns, fireflies and bees!

Can you spot?

Queen of the Fairies   Stardust   Moonlight   cupcake tower

2 owls   4 jugs of pink fizzler   5 lily-pad dresses   6 rainbow fairies   7 dragonflies

Answers

Unicorn Land

Queen of the Unicorns ○
Blossom ○○
Rainbow Shine ○○○
Sparkle ○○○○
3 bunnies ○○○
5 white doves ○○
6 owls ○○
7 blue baby unicorns ○○
8 water fairies ○○

Treetop Travels

Teapot house ○
Wizard Whizzbang ○○
Madame Make-a-lot ○○○
2 gnomes ○○○○
3 pots of nettle soup ○○○○○
4 red squirrels ○○○○
5 swinging pixies ○○○○○
6 dusting fairies ○○
7 wizard flags

Answers

Once Upon a Time

Little Red Riding Hood ⭕
Goldilocks ⭕⭕⭕
The Big, Bad Wolf ⭕⭕⭕⭕
Humpty Dumpty ⭕⭕⭕
The Wicked Witch ⭕⭕⭕
2 handsome princes ⭕⭕⭕
3 little pigs ⭕⭕⭕
5 gingerbread men ⭕⭕⭕
9 princess crowns ⭕⭕

Cloud Magic

Cloud Wizard ⭕
Sunshine Fairy ⭕⭕⭕
an angry elf ⭕⭕⭕⭕
Rainbow Bird ⭕⭕⭕
2 lollipop trees ⭕⭕⭕
3 baby dragons ⭕⭕⭕
4 sleeping pixies ⭕⭕⭕
5 cloud fairies ⭕⭕⭕
8 cloud candy sticks ⭕⭕

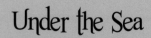

Under the Sea

King Neptune ⭕
Princess Atlanta ⭕⭕⭕
Splash ⭕⭕⭕⭕
Luna ⭕⭕⭕
Gem ⭕⭕⭕
2 treasure chests ⭕⭕⭕
3 pink seahorses ⭕⭕⭕
4 snappy lobsters ⭕⭕⭕
5 baby narwhals ⭕⭕

Answers

Magic Spells

Madame Moonlight ○○○
a skeleton
a sleeping wizard ○○○○
Wanda Witch ○○○○
5 black cats ○○○○○
6 jars of frogs ○○○○○○
7 bubbling cauldrons ○○○○○○○
8 broomsticks ○○○○○○○○
10 pumpkins

Ice World

The Ice Queen ○○○
Princess Star ○○○○
Frosty ○○○○
Snow Bear ○○○○
2 purple pixies ○○○○○○
4 snowflake fairies ○○○○○○
5 twinkling diamonds ○○○○○○○
7 baby penguins ○○○○○○○○
8 frosty cupcakes

Home, Sweet Home

Queen of the Fairies ○○○
Stardust ○○○○
Moonlight ○○○○
cupcake tower ○○○○
2 owls ○○○○○○
4 jugs of pink fizzler ○○○○○○
5 lily-pad dresses ○○○○○○○
6 rainbow fairies ○○○○○○○
7 dragonflies

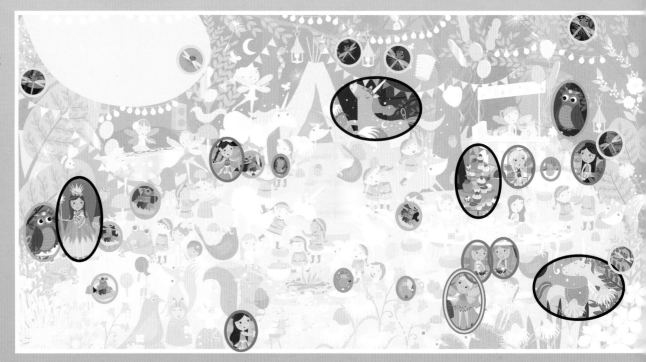